# Eating Disorders

 caring for yourself and others

PASTORAL · OUTREACH · SERIES ·

# Eating Disorders

 caring for yourself and others

Julie Jeffs

redemptorist
p u b l i c a t i o n s

Published by Redemptorist Publications
Alphonsus House, Chawton, Hampshire, GU34 3HQ, UK
Tel: +44 (0)1420 88222, Fax: +44 (0)1420 88805
Email: rp@rpbooks.co.uk, www.rpbooks.co.uk

A registered charity limited by guarantee
Registered in England 3261721

Copyright © Redemptorist Publications 2018
First published September 2018

Series Editor: Sr Janet Fearns
Edited by Kathy Dyke
Designed by Eliana Thompson

ISBN 978-0-85231-522-4

A CIP catalogue record for this book is available from the British Library.

Every effort has been made to trace copyright holders and to obtain their permission for the use of copyright material. The publisher apologises for any errors or omissions and would be grateful for notification of any corrections that should be incorporated in future reprints or editions of this book.

Printed by Lithgo Press Ltd.,
Leicester, LE8 6NU

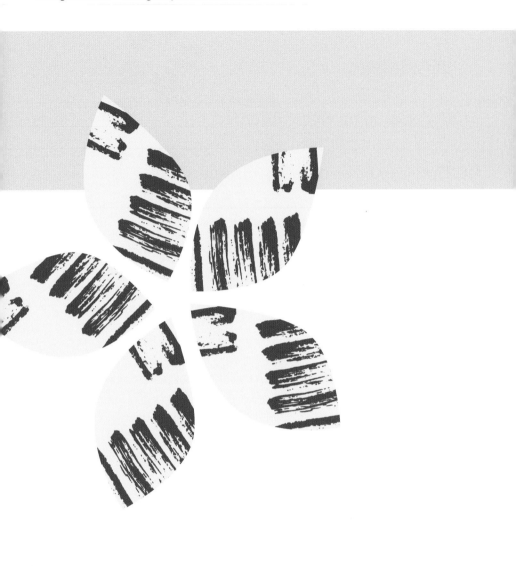

# Introduction

In your pastoral work you will probably meet people who express all sorts of personal and emotional difficulties of more or less apparent severity. You will probably have to decide what help you are able to offer yourself and when you might need to direct someone to more specialist services such as mental health services. Sometimes this won't be an easy decision but usually, either way, patient listening and kind words of support will go a long way towards helping a person, even if they are waiting for more specialist treatment in due course.

This booklet is written to provide a guide in those situations where someone comes to you with a particular sort of difficulty, namely an eating disorder. I would like to explain that I am writing this from both a personal and a professional perspective.

At the age of sixteen (a few decades ago now!) I was given a diagnosis of a severe eating disorder and was admitted to hospital. At the time the support and treatment available was limited and what I was offered just consisted of feeding me up. There was little or no focus on my mental state and how I was feeling did not get explored. Needless to say, when the focus of the treatment is based only on the body, the person is much more likely to return to old self-defeating behaviour.

Later I was able to seek out help that did address my thoughts and feelings as well as my body and I am pleased to say with the right support, over time, I reached a full recovery. Subsequently I went onto train as a psychotherapist, couples therapist and family therapist. I have since worked with many people, of all ages, with different types of eating disorders. Although certain types of eating disorders display similar symptoms, each person's experience is unique and what works for one person might not work for another. Recovery from an eating disorder is possible and research has shown that the earlier someone asks for and receives help, the greater the chance of a positive outcome.

My primary aim here is to help clergy and pastoral workers to better understand eating disorders and feel confident in how they might provide support and guidance when needed.

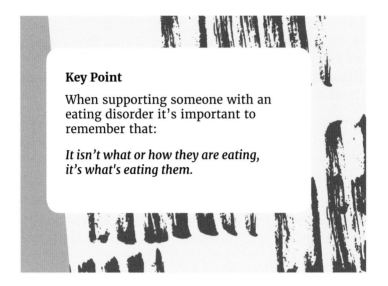

**Key Point**

When supporting someone with an eating disorder it's important to remember that:

*It isn't what or how they are eating, it's what's eating them.*

"Patient listening
and kind words of
support will go a long
way towards helping
a person, even if they
are waiting for more
specialist treatment
in due course."

1

# Understanding eating disorders

Although someone with an eating disorder may appear to have a problem just with food, it is very likely that there are underlying issues which are hard for them to acknowledge. So their relationship to food could be seen as an expression of their internal emotional world.

Often sufferers use food as a remedy for their feelings about their life. In the same way as a person might drink alcohol to ease their feelings about their problems, a person may use food to do the same. In either of these scenarios, a person's emotions may be temporarily eased, but the core problems and issues may be left unaddressed. For example, the person who restricts food is likely to be struggling with a need to try to control some aspect of their world and their feelings, while the person who binges large amounts of food and then purges (ridding the body of that food) through self-induced vomiting, taking laxatives or excessive exercising, may be expressing some difficulty "stomaching" some aspects of their experience. Purging can be a way of trying to cleanse uncomfortable feelings and managing feelings of anger and fear. This condition, of bingeing and purging, is called bulimia nervosa.

People often use food for comfort, but sometimes this can become a very strong habit leading to binge eating and weight problems. Such a person may feel they can't stop eating until they are overly full: this may subdue the difficult feelings and prevent them from feeling overwhelmed. Eating large amounts of food may be a way of stuffing feelings down. It has been suggested by some theorists that every pound of fat is a tear un-cried.

An extreme way of taking control is to eat almost nothing or to stop eating altogether. A person may get to this point through gradually becoming unhappier about the shape of their body and may start by trying out one of the many diets that they see advertised. This may be rewarding, both in the sense of a person feeling that they are doing a good, healthy thing and, also, through the praise and encouragement which they get from other people who may say things like, "You look well."

Comparison with media images of perfect bodies can have a big influence on a person's self-esteem and self-image. These and probably many other influences can perpetuate behaviour which can lead to more extreme and compulsive attempts to control eating. When things reach an extreme a person may literally be starving themselves, while apparently not acknowledging how thin and unhealthy they look. This condition is called anorexia nervosa and can be so serious as to be life-threatening.

Some people are brought up in environments where difficult feelings are not allowed to be expressed. To maintain the balance in the family and protect the family's normal functioning, the sufferer will inevitably have to find a way to manage these difficult feelings alone. All types of eating disorder usually serve to keep the world out and feelings in.

It is not unusual for the sufferer to have made attempts, prior to developing their eating disorder, to have difficult conversations about painful issues and feelings. These conversations have usually been shut down by other family members or have been perceived, by the sufferer, to be judged. This sort of experience can often lead the sufferer to develop an internal belief system that "there isn't anyone there for me". Family systems can work to maintain an eating disorder by shutting down feelings and sweeping difficult issues under the carpet.

## Case study 1: my own experience of anorexia

I started restricting food at the age of fourteen. Many difficult events had occurred in my family of origin, which were all brushed under the carpet. I was a sensitive child and felt things deeply from the onset. I made several attempts to talk to my parents about the depth of my distress and each attempt got stonewalled. I remember feeling insignificant, confused and alone.

Initially the weight loss evoked positive comments from close friends and family which eased my feelings of insignificance and distress. The more weight I lost, the more attention I received from my mother. I had found a way at last to get her attention. The longer I did not eat the more attention my parents gave me and the less time they spent arguing. So I had managed to gain what I needed: support and acknowledgement from those closest to me. The pain of my shrunken body mirrored the pain of the emotions that I was feeling on the inside.

At no time did any family member ask me how I was feeling or why I had taken such drastic measures to alter my body shape. Their whole focus was on getting me to eat. What my family did not understand was that anorexia had become my ally, the one consistent thing that I could rely on. It was my focus: it stopped me thinking about those difficult events and it made me feel significant and visible. I can fully understand how illogical it must seem, to the outside world, to starve yourself to near-death. But anorexia is not a matter of reasoned concern. It's a matter of life or death.

## Case study 2: bulimia

Belinda is a thirty-eight-year-old single parent. She has raised her daughter (who is now eight years old) single-handed from birth. She has not received any support or maintenance during this time from her child's father.

During the past year her daughter has started asking questions about her father's whereabouts. She has become withdrawn and upset when she sees other children with their fathers. Belinda had expected that this could happen as she got older. She knows where to find her daughter's father.

With the support of counselling, Belinda has made the difficult decision to contact her daughter's father. During this time of uncertainty her relationship with food has changed. When she feels anxious she either restricts food intake or binges and purges. With the support of counselling she has been able to understand the link between food and managing difficult feelings. She has become aware that her eating behaviour is a distraction from having to face her feelings about what is really going on. She feels anxious about what the future might hold in terms of having to share access with her daughter's father. The thought of not being with her daughter full-time evokes strong feelings of fear and anxiety.

During counselling Belinda expresses her concerns about her daughter meeting her father. She talks about her guilt for placing her daughter in the position of being a child of a single parent when she split up with her father. She describes feeling like a bad parent. She acknowledges that bingeing and purging is a way of getting rid of the bad feelings, albeit temporarily. In the short term this coping strategy acts like a sticking plaster.

Having gained this insight, if Belinda is willing and able to continue to talk openly about her feelings and her anxiety and develop healthier coping strategies, there is a strong possibility that her problematic eating behaviour will reduce or even cease.

## Case study 3: binge eating disorder

Mary is morbidly obese. She has a BMI of 48. She has been married for twenty-five years and has adolescent children.

Mary's vast weight is causing several physical and psychological difficulties including high blood pressure, type 2 diabetes, joint problems and a strain on her heart. She feels distressed and obsessed about her ever-increasing weight. Yet she uses food as a comfort and feels her weight to be a protection. She describes her weight as her magic shield. It acts as a defence against people, places and things.

Mary's pattern of eating is known to eating disorder professionals as "grazing". She nibbles food throughout the day and evening and sometimes through the night (often in secret). Constant grazing is her way of pushing down difficult feelings. Mary feels protected and imprisoned by her weight. Her binge eating disorder keeps people away (quite literally). Her weight acts as a barrier between herself and the real world. Understandably, she has difficulties with trust. Although her eating disorder keeps her safe, it prevents her from living a more full, active and satisfying life.

During her childhood her mother had a serious mental health condition. As a result of this she was not able to care for herself, let alone her two children. Mary recalled often arriving home from school cold and hungry.

Her mother spent a great deal of time in bed. Mary described the cupboards in her childhood home as often being empty. Sometimes her evening meal would consist of a cold tin of beans. The house was dishevelled, dirty and disorganised. Mary often felt hungry, bewildered and frightened. She feared for her mother's life, while trying to take care of her younger brother.

Mary started working when she was fourteen. She now had the means to buy the food she craved. She quickly learned that food could be her remedy to manage feelings of anxiety, fear and profound sadness. In order to keep her feelings in check, which enabled her to keep going from day to day, she had to graze continuously.

Mary is desperate to change. She is also terrified of losing the shield that protects her fragile existence. She no longer engages in physical activities with her family. She doesn't eat out as she feels embarrassed about her size. She doesn't go to school events or parents' evening as her children feel embarrassed by her weight. Her weight acts as a cushion between her inner pain and reality. Mary is terrified of being abandoned and rejected.

## Weighing things up

For a person to give up their eating disorder they must first understand what it does for them. They must understand how the eating disorder has supported them in their life. Some sufferers may never have learned to sit with and work through their feelings. They may never have learned to ask for help. If the eating disorder has acted as a reliable ally, then the sufferer is not going to give it up without a struggle. The sufferer has to learn (at their own pace) that feelings can be expressed without disastrous consequences, that difficult conversations can be had and that some people *do* want to help them.

Past events that may have turned them towards the eating disorder need to be addressed, acknowledged and worked through emotionally. Often people with eating disorders have little or no experience of speaking honestly and then being genuinely heard. So initially, it is often best to just listen with kindness and compassion. People with eating disorders judge themselves harshly. Offering a non-judgemental listening ear can support the person to be able to take the first step to recovery.

## Making contact and offering support

You may become aware, in a range of circumstances, that somebody might have an eating disorder:

- A person may come to you to discuss an unrelated problem and you notice they are extremely thin and unhealthy looking.

- A relative might bring a person to you because of their concern about their eating behaviour.

- You may observe a member of your congregation who seems very thin or very overweight.

- You may notice things about a person's behaviour – they seem very withdrawn, they don't eat and drink in the presence of others, or they may excuse themselves and leave immediately after eating.

However this person's difficulties come to your attention, the first step, being able to support and help them yourself or direct them to more expert help, will involve establishing trust. Because people with eating disorders often try very hard to hide their problem and may feel a considerable amount of shame, establishing trust may take time and patience.

Your training in pastoral care may well have prepared you for the task of establishing trust. However, when working with some people with eating disorders, the task of balancing your own anxiety and your desire to help as quickly as possible (on the one hand) against the need to go at the pace the person can manage (on the other hand) may be very demanding. This may be the sort of thing that you can take to your own mentor or supervisor or talk through with a trusted colleague. All good therapists and counsellors make use of such discussions regularly, to reflect on their own emotional reactions and to help them achieve and maintain balance in their work.

Once a person feels safe enough to talk freely you may notice that they will either talk about food and their weight and nothing else or the opposite, steering clear of any mention of food, eating or the changes in their body weight. Both of these conversational styles serve to avoid making connections and gaining a deeper self-awareness which otherwise might lead to change.

There are three types of eating disorders:

- anorexia nervosa;

- bulimia nervosa;

- binge eating disorder.

In the next chapter I will focus on each of these individually.

"Anorexia had become my ally, the one consistent thing that I could rely on... it made me feel significant and visible."

2

# The three types of eating disorders

*1. Anorexia nervosa*

**Common signs of anorexia nervosa:**

- a sole focus on being thin or becoming thinner;
- skipping meals or saying they have eaten more than they have;
- excessive calorie counting/avoiding food that is fattening;
- obsessive behaviour around food;
- excessive exercising;
- social withdrawal and isolation.

**Psychological signs:**

- denial about the seriousness of the problem and an extremely distorted view of body image;
- anxiety, low self-esteem and difficulty concentrating;
- perfectionism and setting very high standards for themselves.

**Physical signs:**

- extreme weight loss which can lead to symptoms such as physical weakness, tiredness, dizziness and digestive complaints.

Because anorexia nervosa can develop to the point where it becomes life-threatening this, understandably, provokes anxiety in relatives and friends. They, in turn, may try to remedy the situation by attempting to control the person's eating habits. Food can become the main focus of communication within the family, or group of friends, to the exclusion of other interests and activities.

## 2. *Bulimia nervosa*

### Common signs of bulimia nervosa:

- The person is unable to tolerate large amounts of food and purges through vomiting, uses laxatives or diuretics and fasts. This is often accompanied by over-exercise.

- The person struggles with an impulse to consume large amounts of food (and perhaps alcohol) which may trigger the fear of gaining weight. This makes for the vicious circle described above and a preoccupation with food over all other aspects of life. A telling sign is that the sufferer may disappear soon after eating in order to purge.

- Social withdrawal and mood swings are common and the sufferer may feel intense guilt and shame, despising themselves and their impulses to the extent that they may self-harm.

- A range of physical health difficulties can follow from this cycle of behaviour including digestive problems, tiredness, damage to teeth and difficulty in sleeping.

Despite these difficulties a person with bulimia may succeed in holding their life together to the extent that people may not be aware of their difficulties. This has a two-edged outcome as the person is able to keep their struggle secret (which they may wish to do), but also makes it less likely that people will come forward to help so that they might then break the cycle.

## 3. Binge eating disorder

### Common signs of binge eating disorder:

- Binge eating disorders consist of excessive and disorganised behaviour. A person may feel relatively at ease only when they feel full.

- Life may well be organised around buying lots of food and episodes of binge eating. They eat very rapidly whether or not they are hungry.

- They may be very aware of putting on weight, becoming larger than they would wish and may regret this; yet they are still unable to restrict their eating behaviour.

- They may feel a lack of confidence and self-esteem and may experience shame and guilt, particularly after bingeing.

- They are likely to develop an unhealthy body weight leading to other physical health problems – for example, they may suffer from digestive difficulties, tiredness and diabetes.

- In conjunction with being overweight, they may develop a defensive persona of a happy clown, despite perhaps feeling sad and desperate underneath.

- They may suffer from extreme social anxiety and find their body size a very real embarrassment in a variety of circumstances.

People who develop eating disorders tend to be perfectionists and often set very high standards for themselves, which they feel bad for failing to live up to. A person suffering from any of these eating disorders may find it hard to maintain their educational and/or employment endeavours. This, in turn, can lead to a vicious circle with more and more focus on issues of food and weight, as there are fewer other things in the person's life to engage them.

3

# Capacity and readiness for change

There is a way of thinking about the different stages that a person may go through on their path to acknowledging any difficulty in their life and being able to do something to tackle it. This comes from a helping technique called motivational interviewing.[1] You might find it helpful in trying to understand where a person is in terms of their readiness for change. This approach identifies five stages on the road to change.

## 1. Pre-contemplation stage

Clients at this stage are not even thinking about making a change. They show no intention of changing their behaviour and appear unaware or under-aware of problems.

At this stage, people who have close contact with the sufferer may have started to notice habits and changes in the person concerned. This could be a family member or friend, or it could be somebody like yourself, with a pastoral care responsibility. The person who notices these things might be quite alarmed. They may be concerned about the weight loss they have observed or other habits and behaviour, such as vomiting after meals or avoiding eating.

Despite the best efforts of those around, the sufferer may be unable to acknowledge or talk about their struggle. This creates a dilemma for anybody who is concerned for the sufferer, and is perhaps feeling very anxious and wanting to help before the sufferer is ready. Often at this stage conflicts can arise that might make it harder to establish the rapport necessary for a trusting and helpful relationship. The best that the caring person can do is to contain their own anxiety and concern so as not to be pushy towards the sufferer but still maintain a presence of gentle, sensitive interest in the person's welfare. This might initially best be expressed in general terms rather than any specific reference to food, weight and related issues.

The sufferer needs to feel accepted as they are and welcomed into a supportive, caring environment. If this happens the sufferer may themselves start to raise their own concerns, which might be about food and weight but equally might be about their present or past relationships and emotional struggles. At the point where you feel some trust has been established, you might try to ask gentle questions or to express your concerns in a non-judgemental, gentle manner. Try to phrase these things in terms of your observations and concerns rather than questions and judgements about the sufferer. For example, "I have been a bit concerned about you and I thought that you weren't looking so well lately."

The next steps will depend on the person's response and your sense of what they are ready and prepared to talk about. This is likely to be a very difficult stage, striking a balance between gentle concern/enquiry on the one hand, and not driving the person away because they feel intruded upon or judged on the other. Obviously, each helper will find their own style of managing this balance but in general it is important not be discouraged by slow progress and a sense of taking two steps forward and one step back.

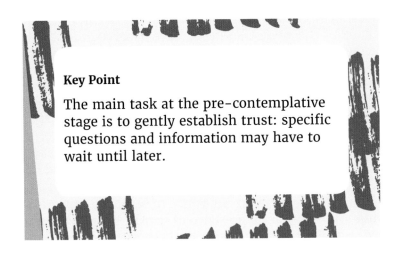

**Key Point**

The main task at the pre-contemplative stage is to gently establish trust: specific questions and information may have to wait until later.

## 2. Contemplation stage

Clients at this stage are beginning to consider making a change but are not yet ready to make a commitment to that change. They will be aware of the problem and be seriously considering the need to change, but with no commitment to take action.

Here the helper's task is to guide the person towards becoming more aware of the different aspects of the problem; for example to explore positive and negative aspects of their relationship with food. Then the person can be helped to think about whether and in what way they would like to change and about how their present behaviour differs from that aim.

The helper can support and gently encourage the person's aspirations to change. It's here that the person's faith may provide additional support for their motivation and confidence to try to change. Questions to ask the person might be:

- How much do you want to change?

- Does someone else want you to change?

- Are you confident that you could succeed?

- Do you think changing will require a lot of effort?

## 3. Preparation stage

Clients in this stage are preparing for action to change in the foreseeable future. The person has a wish to change and may be already trying to make small changes. The helper's task is to encourage these steps and to help the person to strengthen their process of change by making a clear plan of the steps they wish to take in changing. It is at this stage that setting up regular meetings with the person concerned might be helpful.

The helper could encourage the person to consider how committed they are to changing and to think about the different possible supports to change (in addition to that from the helper). Additional support may come from self-help groups, online resources and written material designed to guide the process of change for people with these difficulties. They could also be encouraged to think about whether a friend or family member might be a suitable ally or buddy during the process of change.

It is also important for the person to consider obstacles to change and whether there are people in their life whose behaviour might work against their wish to change. This can happen without there being any such intent, it may (for instance) simply arise out of the habitual attitudes and behaviour towards food of particular other people. Questions to ask the person might be:

- Who are the people in your life at present?

- Of these, who do you think may be able to support you?

- How could they do this?

- Is there anyone who could make it harder for you to change?

## 4. Action stage

Clients in this stage will be actively implementing a plan for change, now the person has decided to take decisive action to change. The helper's task is to support the individual in keeping to their plan, make suggestions, encourage and reinforce changes and support them through obstacles and setbacks.

As someone starts to change and reduce their problematic eating/ not eating habits, they are likely to have to deal with difficult internal struggles as well. It's not unusual for a person to lapse and have a cycle of progress and setbacks. If they judge themselves harshly for their lapses, this can make it harder for them to resume their efforts to change. So, as far as possible the helper needs to encourage a non–judgemental attitude to the progress of change.

It is very common when someone starts to change their eating behaviour for them to be confronted with very strong emotions which the eating behaviour has worked to hide and bury. This can be a very frightening experience and, almost by definition, the stronger and more self-damaging the problematic behaviour is, the stronger will be the emotions which are likely to erupt. So, it is important to reassure the person that (however difficult it feels) this is actually a positive step in the process of change. They may need time to talk about and express the emotions that they become aware of and perhaps to acknowledge the origins of these feelings, which may be in their recent life and relationships or may be far back in their childhood.

This is often a very difficult stage for the individual as they will be learning new ways of balancing strong distressing emotions alongside taking consistent practical steps to change their behaviour. The helper may be able to assist in this process by offering personal support and encouragement in both aspects: the reawakening of difficult emotions and the consistent taking of practical steps to change in the face of these emotions.

Here it would be helpful for the person to have a clear method of recording and measuring the steps of their change, for example a food diary, a journal of emotions and experience, a weight chart, a gratitude diary and a daily list of positive changes. Different people will find these methods more or less helpful and they will provide the helper with varied opportunities for feedback and encouragement. Here a person's faith, trusted allies and the wider community may offer additional and differing levels of support.

Some helpful exercises for the person might be to:

- consider the plus side of their eating behaviour by writing down how it makes them feel good, physically, socially, emotionally, in their relationships with others and in their work;

- write a thank you letter to their eating disorder;

- consider the downside of their eating behaviour by writing down how it makes them feel bad, physically, socially, emotionally, in their relationships with others and in their work;

- write a letter to the eating disorder as their enemy, describing what it has taken away from them;

- draw a road map of their life up until now, showing significant events and milestones;

- draw a road map of their life as it might have been if they had not developed an eating disorder;

- write a letter from the future (say, in four years' time) to anyone from their past or present with an update on what they have done since leaving their eating disorder behind;

- write a letter to the same person, after the same period of time, as though they still had an eating disorder;

- consider what problems they had before developing an eating disorder;

- make a list of the things they value in their life;

- consider the plus and down sides of their eating. For each positive and negative that they have noted, consider whether or not this was part of their personality before their eating problems began. For example, "Nowadays, I never want to see my friends." Were they sociable previously? "I don't want to buy myself nice clothes." Did they take an interest in their appearance previously? And so on.

The following worksheet may also be helpful.

# WORK SHEET: Plans for change

| Plans for change | | |
|---|---|---|
| The changes I want to make are: | | |
| The steps I plan to take in changing are: | | |
| The ways others can help me are: | Person | Ways to help |
| The most important reasons why I want to make these changes are: | | |
| I will know my plan is working if: | | |
| Some things that could interfere with my plan are: | | |
| Notes | | |

## 5. Maintenance stage

Clients in this stage are maintaining the healthy lifestyle changes that they have made. The helper's task is to help the person avoid relapse and to consolidate the gains they have made. Also, the helper's task is to support continued change, which might include learning different ways of dealing generally with life situations, developing new problem-solving skills and learning to process emotions in a constructive and creative way.

At this stage it is useful for the person to identify people, places and things which could present the risk of triggering a relapse. They may need to learn new ways of dealing with these. In particular this might include developing the ability to be assertive and to say "No" to things they don't want.

It is in the nature of eating disorders and other psychological difficulties that the risk of relapse is common. It is to be expected rather than to be seen as a rare and disastrous incidence of failure. At times of stress we all have a tendency to revert to cruder, simpler and less sophisticated ways of dealing with situations.

The next task is to identify what is happening and work towards re-establishing more constructive and creative solutions rather than blaming, criticising and harbouring feelings that one has failed. Helping a person review their progress by asking the following questions can be a useful exercise.

- Are they eating regularly and no longer starving themselves and bingeing?

- Are they being secretive around food?

- Are they beginning to understand when and why they are hungry and actually starting to tune into hunger signals?

- As they gradually decrease foods that have a high fat content, are they beginning to acquire a taste for less fattening foods?

- Are they eating a balanced selection of foods including protein and carbohydrates? Has their guilt around eating carbohydrates decreased?

- Are they enjoying the experience of eating? Are they eating until they feel satisfied? Are their heads or their bodies letting them know when they are full?

- Is their self-worth determined by who they truly are, rather than the number on the scales?

- Are they feeling more energetic and content with themselves?

- Are they starting to use the skills that they have learned to combat automatic eating and to use confrontation to deal with the times when they want to eat even though they are not physically hungry?

- Are they starting to participate in social activities and actually enjoying them?

- Are they more aware of what, when and how they are eating?

- Are they reaching out to people when they are struggling or starting to be isolated?

The process of taking steps towards recovery is well illustrated in the following poem.

## My journey back to self

You were my friend,
my ally,
my consistency,
the thing I turned towards when I felt upset.
You helped me stop feeling.
You never let me down.

In the beginning you made me feel better.
People commented on the weight loss.
I felt as if I was good at something.
I felt in control of my emotions.

As time went on I began to feel worse.
People made negative comments about my weight.
I started to feel unwell.
I felt frightened of change.
I felt frightened of feeling the emotion that was locked away.

And then something happened.
I found the courage to reach out.
I asked for help and the help came.
Friends, family and health care professionals believed I could get better.

At first, it was an uphill struggle but I kept going.
I wanted to be free again:
free from my eating disorder,
free from pain (physical and emotional).

Recovery is possible.
It takes time and it's worth it.
You're worth it.

Thank you to all the people who helped me to get better.
I am so much more than my eating disorder.
I am proud of what I've achieved.

*Julie Jeffs* [2]

## *Endnotes*

1. Massachusetts Behavioural Health Partnership, "Motivational Interviewing – Stages of Change": https://www.masspartnership.com/pdf/MotivationalInterviewingStagesofChange.pdf. See also R.W. Miller and S. Rollnick, *Motivational Interviewing: helping people change*, 3rd edition (New York: Guildford Press, 2012) and C.R. Rogers, *Client-Centred Therapy* (London: Constable & Robinson, 1951, reprinted 2003).

2. See also the poem "Autobiography in Five Short Chapters" by Portia Nelson, from Portia Nelson, *There's a Hole in My Sidewalk: the romance of self-discovery* (Oregon: Beyond Words Publishing, 2012).

4

# Guidance for friends and family

Eating disorders can take over not only the sufferer's life but the life of those around them. Living with someone with an eating disorder can evoke feelings of anxiety, anger and distress. Family members, friends and teachers can struggle with many of the behaviours that have been described in chapter 2 of this booklet.

The person with the eating disorder may cause disarray at mealtimes by not eating, over-eating or leaving the room straight after dinner. If the sufferer's distress isn't acknowledged the family might experience tension and a sense of walking on eggshells. Sometimes family members have a tendency to say nothing for fear of saying the wrong thing and this can increase the underlying anxiety for all concerned.

Sometimes the sufferer may try to control what happens during mealtimes in terms of what is eaten, portion size and what time dinner is served. This can evoke anger in family members as they can feel they are being controlled or coerced by the sufferer and their eating disorder.

Family members may respond to the sufferer by going along, unquestionably, with changes in family eating habits which fit around the sufferer's disordered eating behaviour. While this is understandable, it can have the effect of strengthening the sufferer's compulsions and restricting habits around food.

It is likely to be most helpful if, as far as possible, family members establish and maintain regular mealtimes which the sufferer is invited to join although without coercion. It's important that mealtimes don't become a battle around what the sufferer is and isn't eating. If the family do not come together in their support of the sufferer, this can lead to arguments between family members, particularly between parents. Finding the right balance of support, not ignoring the eating disorder but not putting it in the spotlight may be difficult, particularly if family members are anxious to try to improve things.

It's important to remember that the person is not just their eating disorder. It's vital not to lose sight of all their other qualities, interests and aspects. As far as possible, it's crucial for the family and the individual concerned to try to keep these many qualities actively in mind.

Preparing and serving food can be an act of love and bonding for many families. If the sufferer starts to refuse food that has been lovingly prepared it can feel like a rejection of the family. It's important, wherever possible, not to let these feelings trigger a row, but family members may need help with their own feelings about this. It might help them to talk to the pastoral helper or others about their own feelings.

Psychological suffering in a family can create a whirlpool effect where, more and more, all that gets talked about is the "problem", the eating disorder. This can be a very strong tendency but it's very important that this whirlpool of an eating disorder doesn't lead to the very real everyday conflicts and difficulties between family members being avoided and not discussed and sorted.

It is helpful for family members to learn that people with an eating disorder do not consciously choose to have it and that they have lost the capacity to exert control over their eating behaviour. It is a complex and often entrenched mental health issue. The conversation is likely to be more relaxed and productive in situations where all those involved are feeling comfortable. So it is is not a good idea to have a conversation about food during or just after a meal.

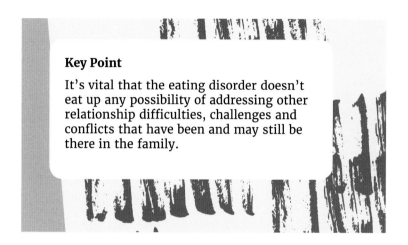

**Key Point**

It's vital that the eating disorder doesn't eat up any possibility of addressing other relationship difficulties, challenges and conflicts that have been and may still be there in the family.

Each person and each family will have its own style of talking and discussing things. Here are some dos and don'ts that might help guide a conversation when trying to help someone with an eating disorder.

## Don't:

- argue, lecture or persuade with logic;

- assume an authoritarian role;

- give expert advice at the beginning;

- order, direct, warn or threaten;

- do most of the talking;

- get into debates or struggles over labelling;

- make moral statements, criticise, preach or judge;

- ask a series of (for instance, three) questions in a row;

- tell your family member/friend/client that they have a problem;

- prescribe solutions or a certain course of action.

## Do:

- let your family member/friend/client present the argument for change or staying the same. Give them the opportunity to talk about, and hopefully, explore their ambivalence;

- focus on your family member/friend/client's concerns;

- emphasise that your family member/friend/client has the choice and the responsibility for deciding their future behaviour;

- explore and reflect upon your family member/friend/client's perception of the situation;

- reflect back what you think you have heard, using statements starting with "I understand you to say";

- summarise periodically;

- aim to be as warm and as caring as possible – be aware of any hostility and criticism;

- admit that you make mistakes;

- avoid saying "but": "and" is far better!

- be prepared to talk about your role in keeping the eating disorder going;

- always weigh up the pros and cons of listening and talking and see how much you have gained.

If the family has been able to discuss the person's struggle with eating and perhaps even some of the underlying emotional turmoil, it might be possible to start to discuss what further help could be sought. The starting point for getting professional help is usually the GP. Some discussion about whether the person concerned would like a family member, or perhaps someone else like the pastoral helper or a close friend, to accompany them is important at this stage. Whether they would like to attend alone or go with a family member will vary from person to person and family to family.

It might be helpful for those concerned to discuss the advantages and disadvantages of either arrangement. On the one hand it is important to respect the person's choice and autonomy but the powerful nature of eating disorders can make it hard for sufferers to acknowledge how much they need help. Having someone to accompany them at this crucial stage, even if that person stays in the waiting room, can make a big difference. The person might be very frightened inwardly but hiding this so don't underestimate the reassurance your presence might provide.

Eating disorder sufferers can be extreme in the degree to which they underplay the seriousness of their condition. It's important that those trying to help do not themselves underestimate the potential seriousness of the condition. At the same time carers need to find a balance so that their own anxiety and desire to change things doesn't turn into extreme coercion (see the list of dos and don'ts on page 34).

Encouraging the person to write down their symptoms and behaviour and a list of any questions they might have for the GP is a useful preparation. At this crucial stage, trying to find a balance between support and encouragement and coercion and control may be difficult. Talking about this dilemma may, in itself, help the process move forward.

## Case study 4: unresolved grief

Mary is twenty-seven. She has been struggling with low weight and control around food for the past five years. On further investigation it comes to light that Mary's father passed away suddenly six years ago. Mary was very close to her father. They shared a similar sense of humour and had a great deal in common. The circumstances around her father's death were difficult. Mary did not have the opportunity to say goodbye to him and wonders if she could have done more to prevent his death.

Mary lives with her mother. She has few friends and spends the majority of her free time either in the house or shopping with her mum. Both Mary and her mum appear not to have dealt with the devasting impact of losing her father. Mary's eating difficulties have become the main focus of their relationship. They spend a considerable amount of time trying to manage Mary's anxiety around food. They cook and shop together.

They do not openly talk about the distress that they both feel in relation to losing Mary's dad. Rather than address their mutual grief at losing a significant person, they use the eating disorder as a focus and a distraction.

Mary and her mother feel frightened about what the future might hold. Mary is concerned about her mother being on her own. Her mother is concerned about Mary being on her own if anything should happen to her. The culture in the family is not to talk about or express difficult emotions. Mary and her mother are locked together in their unresolved grief. Both Mary and her mother are lonely, frightened and isolated. The eating disorder acts as a major distraction from their grieving and it gives them something to focus on daily.

In order for Mary to recover she will need to find a safe space, away from her mum, to talk about her grief. She needs to develop an identity that isn't connected to her eating disorder. If Mary and her mum can find the courage to separate (physically and emotionally) they might be able to feel the impact of the enormous gap that has been left (on the inside and the outside).

It may also be helpful, at some point, for Mary and her mother to engage in family therapy. It is clear that unresolved grief has bonded them together in ways that restrict both their lives. If they are to make progress individually and collectively they will need therapeutic support and guidance.

## Case study 5: comfort eating

John is nineteen and studying architecture at a university away from his home town. John is the first person in his family to attend university. He has struggled to make friends and feels rather isolated and lonely. He feels a lot of pressure, from his family, to succeed. He is known in the family as "the golden child". His family appear to ride on the back of his success. They constantly talk about their hopes for his future. John sometimes feels that he is living someone else's life rather than his own.

John's course is particularly challenging, both mentally and academically. He isn't enjoying the subject. He wanted to go to art college, but his family had other ideas. John has always wanted to please his family and thought going to university would make them proud.

Prior to leaving home his mother took care of all his needs. Now, he is struggling to stay on top of his self-care. His lodgings are increasingly untidy. He is behind with his washing. He feels disorganised and out of control. As John's cooking skills are limited, he is over-dependent on fast food and take-away meals. This has resulted in him putting on weight, a factor which is impacting on his self-esteem. John's mood is low. He is sleeping a lot, missing lectures, watching a considerable amount of TV and comfort eating. John has stopped going home as he doesn't want his family to know that he is failing at his course. He also feels embarrassed by his weight gain.

Because of his difficult emotions, John appears to be in a vicious circle of feeling bad and eating. He is fearful of telling his family the truth as he doesn't want to let them down. It is likely that he is struggling with depression. John has developed a repetitive cycle of feeling sad/bad and comfort eating to make himself feel better. As comfort eating only provides temporary relief it is likely to continue until the underlying issues are addressed.

In this case, John's first point of call needs to be to register with the GP to consider if he is suffering from clinical depression. Each university has a student counselling service which John could access for help and support. The student counselling service would encourage/support John to contact his university lecturer with a view to obtaining an extension of his course deadlines for extenuating circumstances.

During the counselling sessions John would be offered the space to talk through his real concerns regarding his fear of failure, family pressure, letting his family down and low self-esteem in a non-judgemental environment. As John gains control of his studies and the direction of his life, makes sense of his internal distress and speaks openly about his feelings, his binge eating is likely to decrease.

## Case study 6: deep-seated anger

Ben has been struggling with bulimia for five years. His weight is within the normal weight range for his height.

Ben is the youngest sibling in his family. His father has a serious drink problem. Ben is a sensitive young man who worries constantly about his father's health. His mother uses him as a confidant to talk through and express anger about her husband's drinking. Ben finds this deeply upsetting as he hates seeing his mother distressed. It also means he can no longer discuss his own concerns/feelings with his mother as he worries about upsetting her.

Ben's father is also a workaholic. When Ben was growing up his father rarely attended any school activities, including parents' evenings, because he was always working. Ben has come to believe that his father doesn't care about him, an attitude which has had a detrimental impact on his self-esteem.

Ben has expressed the fear that his bulimia feels out of control. He wants to stop although his previous attempts have soon fallen by the wayside. His bulimic behaviour has become the antidote to managing difficult internal feelings. He has learned (through observing his father, who becomes aggressive when he drinks) that expressing strong feelings can hurt those nearest and dearest to you. He has no desire to discharge more anger into his family domain.

Instead he eats large amounts of food and then angrily spews his feelings of disdain into the toilet. This gives Ben a temporary feeling of being in control. He has cleansed himself of the anger that he feels towards his father, mother and very likely himself.

It is not unusual for people struggling with bulimia to have a fear that if it stops they will put on a large amount of weight. This would give them the terrifying feeling of things ballooning out of control.

If Ben can find a safe environment (which might be with a counsellor, mentor, pastoral helper or teacher) where he can talk openly and express his deep-seated anger, his chances of recovery are high. With consistent and ongoing support Ben will learn that he doesn't have to hold it all together for other people. He will come to experience that feelings can be expressed without negative consequences.

As part of his recovery, he will learn the art of meal planning and the importance of structured eating throughout the day. He will be shown healthier strategies to manage sitting with uncomfortable feelings. He will learn the art of relating from a position of authenticity rather than keeping part of himself secret.

### Issues which may be affecting the sufferer:

- avoidance of underlying problems between family members not addressed;

- unresolved grief;

- what can't be expressed or talked about within the family;

- pressure to achieve and high expectations, perhaps to counter the disappointment of previous generations;

- "pass the parcel" or "hot potato" problems (whose problem is it really?);

- competition between family members for love and self-esteem;

- difficulties in dealing with the sufferer changing from childhood to adulthood for both parents and children;

- traditional styles and changing habits of food, meals and diets;

- competition and comparison between families;

- unresolved guilt and shame;

- family beliefs about not "airing your dirty laundry" in public;

- putting on a perfect front for others;
- issues passed from generation to generation;
- relationship difficulties;
- issues around sexuality and self-acceptance;
- low self-esteem;
- fear around growing up and all this entails;
- the desire to be independent and the challenge of over-involved family members;
- difficulties with forming friendships;
- leaving home;
- parents getting a divorce;
- bullying;
- work-related stress.

## Issues which may be affecting the pastoral helper

The pastoral carer may have had a range of experiences previously that have left them with strong feelings and beliefs about abundance and scarcity, poverty and enormous wealth, love, nurture and separation/abandonment. It is important to reflect on and acknowledge how these experiences might impact on trying to help someone whose habitual behaviour appears to abuse both their bodies and an abundant supply of food.

If you have not suffered from an eating disorder (or from other strong obsessions and compulsions) it can be hard to understand, empathise with, and feel compassion about the extent to which these issues can override a person's free will and best intentions. The person may themselves feel great concern for world poverty and scarcity but still have an overriding compulsion to vomit their food down the toilet. As you can imagine, this may leave them with very strong feelings of shame.

In reflecting on their own experience, feelings and reactions, the pastoral carer may well be able to ground themselves in a non-judgemental and compassionate position. Such non-judgemental compassion is a vital foundation for helping a person with such psychological and behavioural difficulties to accept themselves at the first stage of personal change and growth. Paradoxically, psychological change occurs most readily in an atmosphere of self-acceptance.

The pastoral carer may themselves have a family history that has similarities with those of the person coming for help. This may evoke unexpected strong emotional reactions which could influence the quality of their caring relationship.

All of this points to the importance of the pastoral carer having their own supervisor, mentor or trusted colleague with whom they can discuss their experience and reactions within their pastoral work. Such an arrangement is part of the working life of any responsible member of the caring professions. It allows for support and problem-solving but also, at its best, can provide a stimulus for creative and imaginative developments and solutions.

It commonly happens that the despair and isolation of the person coming for help can find itself echoed and reflected in the experience of the helper. Rather than seeing this as showing weakness or inadequacy, it should be considered as a natural occurrence: it takes place within intense, emotional and complex settings and within helping relationships with people affected by eating disorders and other psychological difficulties. This again emphasises the importance of regular meetings with a supervisor, mentor of another trusted colleague for the pastoral carer.

The pastoral carer should expect to feel a whole range of emotions which may be intense and disorientating, but with adequate time and opportunity to reflect and work through these reactions, they should be able to retain their foundation within compassionate, non-judgemental listening.

In addition, there are many practical issues and potential arrangements that can either enhance the carer's effectiveness or reduce it. These include such things as:

- time management;

- finding the time with the pressures of other work;

- having a quiet, private, confidential room where you won't be interrupted;

- finding a balance between privacy and the "need to know" of other people such as parents and medical staff;

- having available all the information that you can gather about organisations and people offering local support;

- being as well-informed as you can be about eating disorders and how to address the issues involved (we hope this booklet will go some way towards addressing that);

- arranging regular meetings with a mentor or supervisor;

- deciding and agreeing with the sufferer what should be communicated and to whom at different stages;

- having the administrative support to be able to do this.

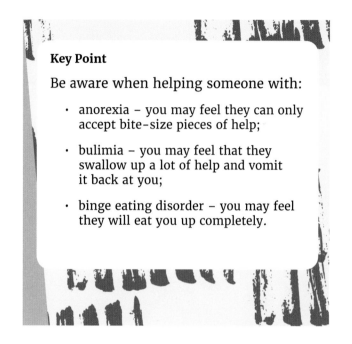

**Key Point**

Be aware when helping someone with:

- anorexia – you may feel they can only accept bite-size pieces of help;

- bulimia – you may feel that they swallow up a lot of help and vomit it back at you;

- binge eating disorder – you may feel they will eat you up completely.

5

# Useful tools for recovery

*Keeping a food diary*

Recovery from an eating disorder takes time. It may have taken years to develop the illness and therefore it is not easy to break established eating habits, especially if they have become a way of coping with emotional difficulties. Re-establishing a structured eating pattern by planning meals is a helpful part of recovery.

It can be helpful for sufferers to complete a set of food diaries, one sheet for each day of the week. This can help the sufferer gain a better understanding of the times when they may be most at risk of reverting to unhelpful eating habits.

Completing a food diary, particularly for the first time, can provide valuable insight and can also evoke strong feelings of sadness, compassion for oneself, guilt and shame.

If the sufferer is restricting food they will see clearly how little they are eating. This can come as quite a shock. For those who binge and/or purge, they clearly see the volume and frequency of their eating and the feelings connected with their behaviour.

The aim of completing a food diary for seven days is not to add judgement about the eating disorder but to consider how and where change might be possible. An important step towards recovery is developing a meal plan. A healthy meal plan consists of breakfast, lunch, dinner and two snacks (one in the morning and one in the afternoon).

This can be done with the help of a dietician or the sufferer's GP will have access to valuable resources connected to the Eatwell campaign. The practice nurse can provide valuable support in the early stages of recovery. See this link for valuable information and resources: https://www.gov.uk/government/publications/the-eatwell-guide

# Food Diary

**Date...................................**

| Time | Food & drink consumed | Regrets? | Binge | Vomit | Lax | How I feel at the moment |
|------|------|------|------|------|------|------|
|  |  |  |  |  |  |  |

| | |
|------|------|
| The desire to starve myself today has been... | Not at all  1   2   3   4   5   6   7   8   9   10  As strong as it could be |
| Today's urge to overeat has been... | Not at all  1   2   3   4   5   6   7   8   9   10  As strong as it could be |
| Today in general I have felt... | Not upset  1   2   3   4   5   6   7   8   9   10  Extremely upset |
| What made me feel good today? | |

## *Starting afresh*

When the sufferer begins to make changes to their eating habits, difficult feelings which had previously been suppressed by the eating disorder can come to the surface. This can be frightening for the sufferer and lapses will occur as they are a definite and important part of recovery. Below is a list of ideas for helping with eating.

### For suffers restricting food intake

- Eat while watching the TV.

- Listen to music while eating.

- Read a book while eating.

- Loudly say "no" to anorexic thoughts while eating.

- Create a story in your head or write while eating.

- Eat with a close friend.

- Ask those eating with you to hold your attention during the meal.

- Create images as you eat (for example, walking from the dark into the light).

- "Hear" your therapist's or pastoral helper's reassuring words as you eat.

### For binge eaters

- Avoid buying trigger foods.

- Replace trigger foods with healthier alternatives (cut up fresh fruit and vegetables and keep them in the fridge).

- Plan meals and use a shopping list.

- Don't shop when hungry.

- Create a flow chart of events leading to a binge.

- Signal the end of meals: brush teeth or eat an orange or a mint.

## How to cope with anxiety after eating

- Ring a friend.
- Go for a walk.
- Go to the bottle bank and smash a few bottles.
- Practise mindfulness.
- Say a prayer.
- Say the Serenity Prayer (see below) several times.
- Read the Bible.
- Practise positive self-talk.
- Attend a twelve-step recovery meeting.
- Read a self-help book.
- Write in your journal.
- Listen to a relaxing piece of music which you like.

### Serenity Prayer

God, grant me the serenity
to accept the things I cannot change;
courage to change the things I can;
and the wisdom to know the difference.

*Reinhold Niebuhr*

In other words, between bingeing and purging, there is a choice to do it differently. In that choice lies your recovery and your freedom from a life with an eating disorder.

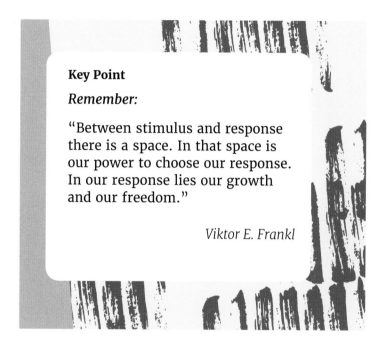

**Key Point**

*Remember:*

"Between stimulus and response there is a space. In that space is our power to choose our response. In our response lies our growth and our freedom."

*Viktor E. Frankl*

## Understanding what triggers a binge

Keeping a diary can be very helpful when trying to identify the triggers that cause you to binge. You could write down your thoughts as well as noting trigger situations, to help you develop a strategy to bring the bingeing under control.

For instance, you may find you are more likely to binge:

- at certain times of the day, maybe when you are home alone in the evenings;

- at certain times of the month. If a woman has bulimia, there may be certain times during the menstrual cycle when a binge is more likely.

- under stress at work, at home or before exams;

- when snack food is around, like crisps, biscuits or chocolate;

- when you have skipped lunch or not eaten for a long time;

- in response to something disturbing that you see or read about, such as child abuse.

It may be difficult to cope with uncomfortable feelings without bingeing. Here are some ways to help control the urge to binge:

- If being home alone is a trigger, you should try and leave the house, go for a walk, telephone a friend or do something you enjoy that is not associated with bingeing.

- Be kind to yourself with a treat such as a massage or a favourite film.

- If you can, allow yourself to sit with the feelings. Writing about your feelings in your journal, or drawing them, can be useful ways of getting them down on paper.

- Seek inspiration in other people's writings, paintings and quotes.

- Take up a new interest, enrol in an evening class or become a volunteer.

- Ensure you get regular exercise; walking once a day is good.

- Re-educate yourself to eat healthily – select low-fat and low-sugar products and snack on fruit and vegetables. Have treats maybe only at weekends.

Remember, recovery from bulimia takes time. It is not easy to break established eating habits, particularly if they have become your way of coping with emotional difficulties. The first step to recovery is acknowledging that you have bulimia and you can get better.

Bulimia tends to throw eating patterns into chaos, so planning meals will help.

- Take it slowly. Begin by planning breakfast each day for a week, then breakfast and lunch and so on.

- Eat regularly – little and often. Six small meals a day may be more suitable. This will help to avoid feeling hungry at a time when you are training yourself in proper eating patterns.

- Try to keep to regular meals, even if you binge and purge.

- Write out meal plans for a week at a time – this will help you not to worry about what to eat and when. You can then allow yourself some flexibility. You must make sure your nutrition is balanced.

- Eat slowly to enjoy different flavours and textures. Putting your cutlery down between each mouthful of food can help with this.

- If you do binge after a meal, try not to write off the whole day. Remember, you can start your healthy eating plan at any time of the day.

- Say the Serenity Prayer (see page 50) regularly throughout the day.

## *Important tools for the journey*

### Listen to what's really eating you

Eating disorders often act as a barrier between a person's experience of reality and their emotional pain. The eating disorder can suppress difficult memories and feelings and become a distraction from what is really going on for the sufferer. Part of recovery consists of helping the sufferer recognise the relationship between feelings and eating.

A journal can be a safe place to write your thoughts and feelings. If you can, find a quiet place where you feel comfortable and won't be disturbed. Write down everything you feel in that moment, including physical sensations in the body, emotions and thoughts. Allow the pen to move freely across the pages. Do not be distracted by spelling mistakes or grammar. Remember, this is your journal. It can include pictures, doodling, random thoughts or you may wish to create a collage of images which capture your experience.

### Talk with someone

Reach out to someone whom you trust. Let them know how you feel by sending them an email. Call the Beat helpline (see page 59).

### Create an emotional toolbox

Find a shoe box and cover it in pretty paper. Inside the box place photographs (of people, places and things) that create happy memories. Include inspirational poems, a favourite book, your favourite prayers, special cards, and anything else that has inspired you throughout the years.

In your toolbox you may wish to include a list of things to do when you are blue such as:

· buy a pair of new jazzy socks;

· feed the birds;

· compile a list of your favourite songs;

- plant flowers;

- take a bubble bath;

- send a postcard to a friend;

- make five wishes;

- finger-paint;

- put on your favourite music and start dancing;

- walk a dog.

## Practise mindful breathing

Start by bringing your attention to your feet. Notice the solidity of the ground underneath your feet. Notice sensations in your toes, notice the spaces in between your toes and the pads of your toes. Notice the sole of your foot and the upper part. Notice the delicate skin covering each foot.

Now notice all the contact points where your body is touching a solid surface. Your feet, your seat (if you are sitting) or your back (if you are lying down). Imagine, with every out breath, your body relaxing and the tension in your body softening.

Now bring your attention to the breath in the body. Notice the rise and fall of your belly as you breathe in and out. Often the belly is a place where we hold tightness and tension. It is sometimes known as our emotional barometer. Imagine, with every out breath, your belly softening/relaxing.

Bring your attention to your chest. Notice the expansion of your chest as you breathe in and your chest contracting as you breathe out. Use your breath as an anchor to bring yourself back to the present moment.

Remember most people can manage the one moment at a time. Practise mindful breathing regularly so it becomes part of your emotional toolbox when you are struggling.

## Develop mindfulness

This is for all the occasions when you notice yourself thinking or acting in ways that move you away from staying well. Take an inventory at the end of each day of what acts of kindness supported your ongoing recovery and what bad habits caused you to suffer unnecessarily. These might include:

- missing exercise routines;
- smoking, eating or drinking too much;
- eating too much junk food;
- isolating yourself;
- getting up or going to bed too late;
- over-working;
- leaving things to the last minute;
- saying "sorry" too often;
- spending more than you can afford;
- not taking lunch breaks;
- talking too much or too quickly;
- not letting others know how you really feel.

The sooner you become aware of these bad habits the sooner you can return to your emotional toolbox and use the strategies that support and enhance your wellbeing.

## Learn to problem-solve

When emotions are running high, cognition usually goes out of the window. This makes rational decision making incredibly hard. Learning to problem-solve is an important skill.

Developing a strategy to problem-solve can be incredibly useful. Below are five simple steps on how to problem-solve.

Step 1:  Define the problem clearly.

Step 2:  Think up solutions: be creative and let your imagination run wild!

Step 3:  Work out the pros and cons for each solution.

Step 4:  Select a solution.

Step 5:  After you have tried it, review its usefulness.

Remember, as with any new skill, learning to problem-solve will take practice. As you practise this new skill your confidence will grow and you will learn to trust your intuition.

6

# Organisations offering support and treatment

## *Beat Eating Disorders*

Beat is the UK's leading charity supporting anyone affected by eating disorders, anorexia, bulimia, EDNOS [Eating Disorder Not Otherwise Specified] or any other difficulties with food, weight and shape. Beat is here to support eating disorder sufferers and their families and campaign on their behalf for better treatment.

Helpline: 0808 801 0677

https://www.beateatingdisorders.org.uk/

## *Overeaters Anonymous*

Overeaters Anonymous is a twelve-step programme for people with problems related to food including, but not limited to, compulsive overeaters, those with binge eating disorder, bulimics and anorexics. People are invited to attend twelve-step recovery meetings and to work a twelve-step programme that offers a new way of life that enables the compulsive eater to live without the need for excess food.

https://www.oagb.org.uk/

# Conclusion and summary

I need to be clear that this book is not intended to turn you into a trained and accredited expert or counsellor in the area of eating disorders. It is expected that those reading this will be working in a setting where they provide pastoral care for many people with a range of different needs, concerns and issues which they may bring. Also, it is expected that you may have received extensive training for this pastoral role. You may even have a foundation of training in counselling or psychotherapy or, alternatively, you may be a newly recruited volunteer just learning the ropes. Whatever your stage of training and experience, I hope that this booklet will give you a deeper understanding of a person in the grip of an eating disorder and will help you to empathise and focus your care (at whatever level) in a way that will be most helpful. Perhaps it will also stimulate you to do some further reading and/or training and so extend your knowledge and skills further.

# Suggested reading

- *What's Eating You?* by Tammy Nelson MS (New Harbinger, 2008). A workbook for teens with anorexia, bulimia and other eating disorders.

- *The Stress Reduction Workbook for Teens* by Gina M. Biegal MA, LMFT (New Harbinger, 2017). A mindfulness skills workbook to help you deal with stress.

- *Anorexia Nervosa: a survival guide for families, friends and sufferers* by Janet Treasure (Psychology Press, 1997). This book includes sections for parents and other carers alongside a section for the sufferer.

- *Getting Better Bit(e) by Bit(e): a survival kit for sufferers of bulimia nervosa and binge eating disorders* by Ulrike Schmidt and Janet Treasure (Routledge, 1993). This self-help book, the efficacy of which has been proven in clinical trials, empowers sufferers to take control of their lives by providing them with the information and advice needed to tackle their eating difficulties.

- *Breaking Free from Compulsive Eating* by Geneen Roth (Penguin, 1993). This book offers reassuring practical advice on breaking the binge–diet cycle for ever.

- *Counselling for Eating Disorders* by Sara Gilbert (SAGE Publications Ltd, 2000). This is a practical and engaging guide to counselling people with eating disorders using cognitive and education techniques to help clients.

- *Skills-based Learning for Caring for a Loved One with an Eating Disorder* by Janet Treasure, Gráinne Smith and Anna Crane (Routledge, 2016). This book will help carers cope better with the challenge of helping loved ones recover from an eating disorder. Although it is intended for carers, it can be a guide for professionals involved in the treatment of eating disorders.

- *Bulimia: a guide to recovery* by Lindsey Hall and Leigh Cohn (Gurze Books, 2010). This book offers accurate information, wise counsel and genuine hope for anyone who suffers with bulimia.

- *Answers to Anorexia: a breakthrough nutritional treatment that is saving lives* by James M. Greenblatt MD (Sunrise River Press, 2013). This book offers a new medical treatment plan for anorexia nervosa.